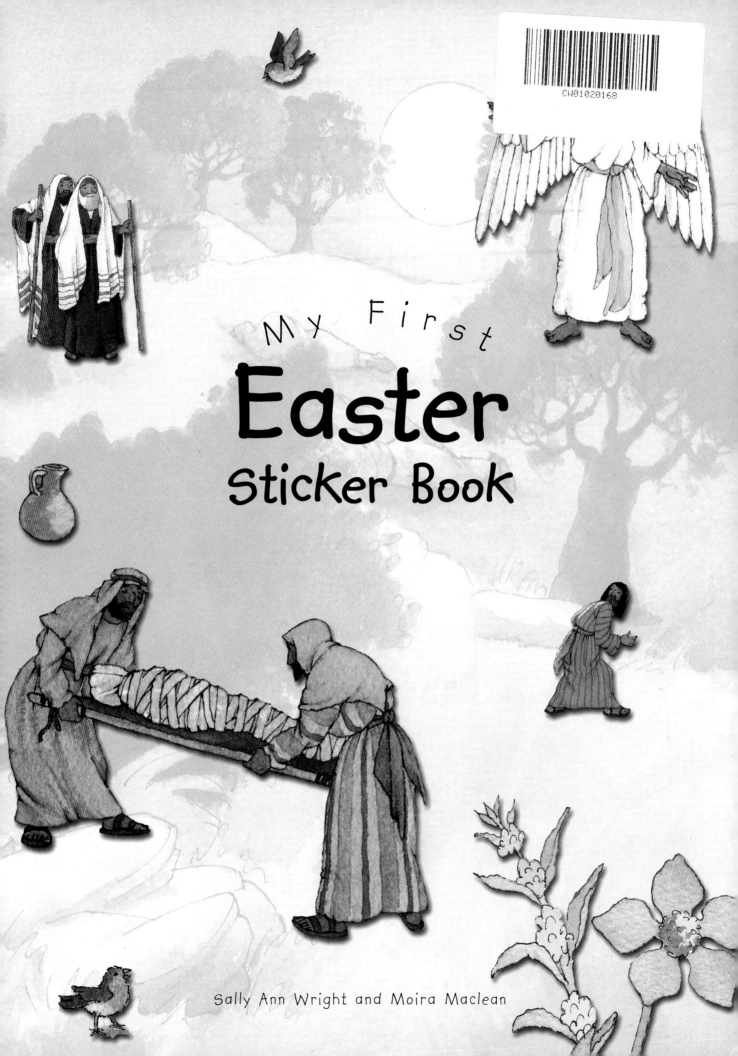

My First
Easter
Sticker Book

Sally Ann Wright and Moira Maclean

Jesus cared about other people.
He healed people with terrible diseases.
He calmed a storm and made sure hungry people
had enough to eat. He showed everyone how
much God loved them.
One day, Jesus and his friends were
going to Jerusalem for the Passover feast.
Jesus told his disciples to go to a man

who had a donkey ready for him.

As Jesus approached the city gates, people were waiting. They couldn't wait to greet him!

Some cut down palm branches and waved them. Others put their cloaks in front of the donkey to make a soft path.

'Hooray for Jesus!' they all shouted. 'Here comes our King!'

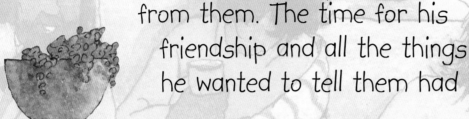

Jesus decided to eat the Passover meal with his special friends in the upstairs room of a house. As they sat round the table together, Jesus explained to them that soon his enemies would come and take him away from them. The time for his friendship and all the things he wanted to tell them had

come to an end. This would be the last time they ate together for a while.

While Jesus was speaking, one of his friends crept out in the dark night. He had been paid to tell the soldiers where to find Jesus. The friend's name was Judas.

After the friends had eaten, they went with Jesus on to a hillside nearby covered with olive trees. It was called the Garden of Gethsemane.

The men were all tired because it was late. But Jesus asked his friends to stay with him while he prayed.

Jesus knew that terrible things would soon happen to him. He prayed to his Father God for help. He asked God to help him to be

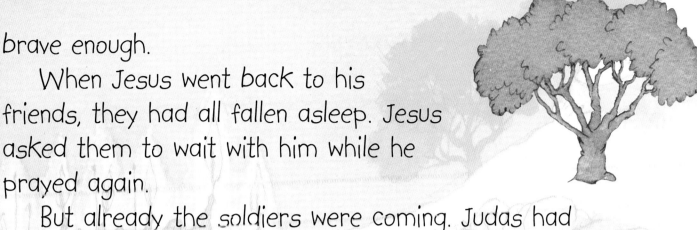

brave enough.
    When Jesus went back to his
friends, they had all fallen asleep. Jesus
asked them to wait with him while he
prayed again.
    But already the soldiers were coming. Judas had
betrayed his friend.

Jesus was arrested by the soldiers. His friends were afraid and ran away. Jesus was marched away to the Roman governor.

Pontius Pilate was not angry with Jesus. He knew Jesus had done nothing wrong. But outside his window there was an angry crowd.

'Crucify Jesus!' the angry men shouted. 'Put him on a cross to die!'

The numbers tell you the page where you should put the sticker.

Where were the people Jesus had helped? Where were all his friends now?

In the crowd were men who were jealous of Jesus. These men paid others to shout and ask for Jesus to be put to death. Their cruel plan was working.

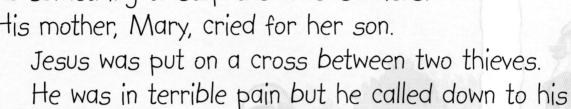

Jesus was taken away to a hill called Calvary. Jesus' friends followed, wishing they could do something to stop the cruel soldiers. His mother, Mary, cried for her son.

Jesus was put on a cross between two thieves. He was in terrible pain but he called down to his

friend John. He asked him to look after his mother as if she was his own mother. Then he asked Mary to treat John as if he were her own son. John and Mary were frightened and sad. They knew that Jesus would die before the day was ended.

Jesus died later that afternoon. Some friends took down his body from the cross and buried it in a cave. Jesus' friend Mary Magdalene watched as they rolled a big stone in front of it.

On Sunday morning Mary went into the garden with a jar of perfume. She wondered who would move the big stone so she could anoint Jesus' body.

But what had happened? Someone had moved the stone. And two angels were there!

'Jesus isn't here,' they told her. 'God has raised him from the dead. Jesus is alive!'

Mary was amazed! Could this be true? Could her friend really have been dead but now be alive again?

ary turned away from the angels, not sure what to do next. She still didn't understand what the angels could mean.

Then Mary looked around and saw a man standing in the garden.

'Please,' she said, thinking it was the gardener, 'do you know where they have taken Jesus?'

The man did not answer her question. He just spoke

her name.

'Mary!' he said.

And all at once Mary knew who it was! This was Jesus, alive and real!

'I am alive,' Jesus told her. 'Go and tell my friends so that they can be happy too!'

So Mary ran to tell them the good news that Jesus was no longer dead but very much alive.

 Barnabas
for
Children®

Barnabas for Children® is a
registered word mark and the logo
is a registered device mark of
The Bible Reading Fellowship.

Published by The Bible Reading Fellowship
15 The Chambers, Vineyard
Abingdon, OX14 3FE
United Kingdom
Tel: +44 (0)1865 319700
Email: enquiries@brf.org.uk
Website: www.brf.org.uk

ISBN 978 1 84101 658 0

First edition 2005
Second edition 2007, reprinted twice 2008
This edition 2013

Copyright © 2005 Anno Domini Publishing
www.ad-publishing.com
Text copyright © 2005 Sally Ann Wright
Illustrations copyright © 2005 Moira Maclean
Editorial Director Annette Reynolds · Art Director Gerald Rogers.
Pre-production Krystyna Hewitt · Production John Laister

British Library Cataloguing in Publication Data.
A catalogue record for this book is available from the British Library.

Printed and bound in China